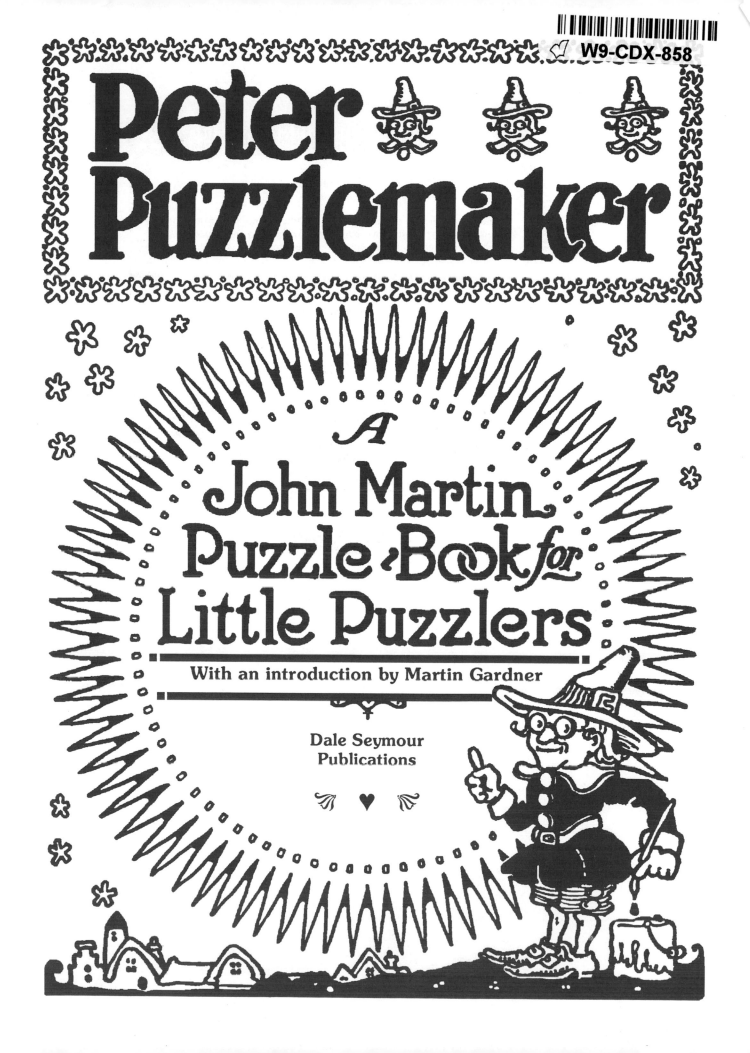

Peter Puzzlemaker

A

John Martin Puzzle Book for Little Puzzlers

With an introduction by Martin Gardner

Dale Seymour
Publications

DALE
SEYMOUR
PUBLICATIONS
P.O. BOX 10888
PALO ALTO, CA 94303

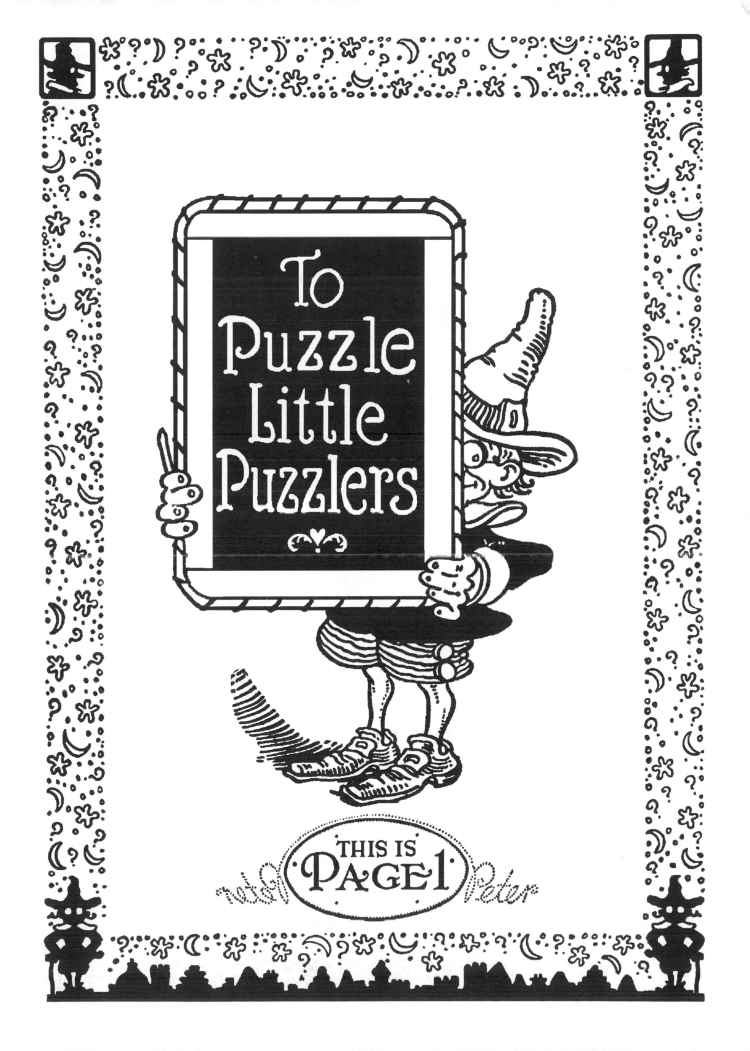

To Puzzle Little Puzzlers

THIS IS PAGE 1

PETER PUZZLEMAKER

◉ DDCTONIAIE ◉

'VE long kind My grew dizzy making your book keep children busy. you To puzzle this In very brain intent; with pondered

But this is by And you pleasure, am and glad all and measure. words Beyond I'm rewarded, I youngsters gives you loved book if

And this helps to With completely will be name *Your* PETER. Puzzlemaker myself to I Proud happiness *think* you book if

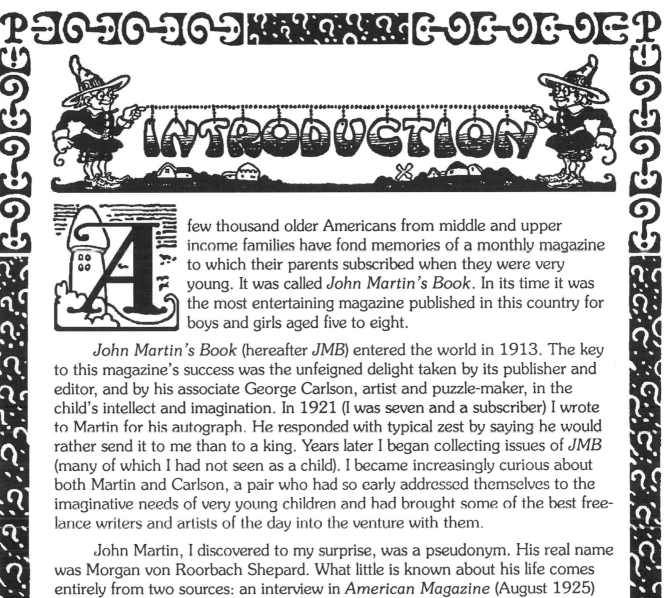

INTRODUCTION

A few thousand older Americans from middle and upper income families have fond memories of a monthly magazine to which their parents subscribed when they were very young. It was called *John Martin's Book*. In its time it was the most entertaining magazine published in this country for boys and girls aged five to eight.

John Martin's Book (hereafter *JMB*) entered the world in 1913. The key to this magazine's success was the unfeigned delight taken by its publisher and editor, and by his associate George Carlson, artist and puzzle-maker, in the child's intellect and imagination. In 1921 (I was seven and a subscriber) I wrote to Martin for his autograph. He responded with typical zest by saying he would rather send it to me than to a king. Years later I began collecting issues of *JMB* (many of which I had not seen as a child). I became increasingly curious about both Martin and Carlson, a pair who had so early addressed themselves to the imaginative needs of very young children and had brought some of the best free-lance writers and artists of the day into the venture with them.

John Martin, I discovered to my surprise, was a pseudonym. His real name was Morgan von Roorbach Shepard. What little is known about his life comes entirely from two sources: an interview in *American Magazine* (August 1925) and three pages by Martin himself in the July 1923 issue of *JMB*. Although Morgan was born in Brooklyn in 1865, his first nine years were spent in poverty on a plantation in Maryland. His mother had married at age sixteen. "She was my playmate, teacher, and mother—all in one," Martin told his interviewer.

> She and I lived in a world of our own; a world where fact and fancy went hand in hand. For instance, in the yard there was a bird house, occupied by a colony of martins. To me they were as real as a human family. . . . My mother talked of them by name: John and Joan, Robin, Alice, and a dozen or so more. John was the leader bird, and their house was John Martin's House. When the birds would return to their home from mysterious flights, they brought back tales of adventure. That was the way my mother taught me geography. Sometimes they were stories of animals and birds and fishes, and so I learned natural history. Or tales of heroes and people who had lived a long time ago, and that was my introduction to

human history. And best of all, these magic martins were intimately acquainted with fairies, and not at all averse to letting me know their secrets.

The death of his "beautiful girl mother" (as Morgan called her in 1923) when he was nine was a crushing blow. He spent years at a boarding school, and then moved restlessly from job to job. While recovering in New York City from an operation on his leg (it had been severely injured when he tried to retrieve possessions from his San Francisco office after the great 1906 earthquake), Morgan began to write and sell poems to children's magazines. Ill-educated and unlucky, torn between rebelliousness and the need to earn a living, he found continuing pleasure in writing long letters to children. His letters would swarm with funny little pictures that illustrated whimsical stories. The letters were signed John Martin, and henceforth we will call him by that name.

In 1908 Martin asked himself: why not turn my letters into a small monthly periodical? With the addresses of a few hundred mothers, he began to solicit subscriptions. The first printed letter, handwritten and illustrated by Martin, went to four subscribers. Soon he was mailing out two thousand.

Printed on tinted paper that varied in color from letter to letter, the contents were intensely personal, loving, sentimental, informal, chatty, and pious. Each letter opened with "My Dear . . ." followed by a space in which Martin would add the child's name. "How do you do?" the first letter began. "I hope you are very well, and as happy as can be. My name is John Martin. I have had quite a good many birthdays, but I never grow very old—my heart stayed young. I can run fast and if I tumble down I get up and laugh some."

One finds in these letters almost all the ingredients that would later go into *JMB*. They anticipated the activity features that would play such a major role: secret codes, riddles, rebuses, puzzles, and pages to be folded or cut. There are sentimental poems and tales about the beauty of nature, fairies, pets, mermaids, and knights, all with a strong emphasis on love and religious faith, though seldom with reference to any particular faith. For moral instruction the letters introduced the Chubbies, well-behaved little children who became a staple feature of *JMB*. The following jingle by Martin, accompanying a picture in the August 1919 issue of Chubbies going off to school, is typical:

> The Chubbies love the life they live
> And all the goodness in it,
> And they are always punctual,
> Exactly on the minute.
> They never waste my time or yours
> And make us wait or worry.
> But still they don't get out of breath
> With needless rush and hurry.

Martin always kept in close touch with his readers. He spent "working vacations," as he called them, on the beaches of Nantucket, where he sat under a large blue umbrella with the initials "J. M." on it. He liked to hide 500 Chinese coins in the sand, offering a prize to the child who found the most. He would give away 500 free tickets for ice-cream cones. "It isn't good sporting to ask for these tickets," he said in his 1925 interview. "Children are natural grafters, but they are better natural sports if you'll give them a chance. If a child *asks* for one, he doesn't get it. Five hundred goodly doings that are *worth* something get as many cone tickets out of me."

After four years of success, Martin changed the name of his periodical from *John Martin's Letters* to *John Martin's Book*. The first issue appeared late in 1912, published by John Martin's House. Pre-1920 issues are now extremely rare. The earliest in my collection, October 1913, has 96 pages on heavy stock, without pagination. Beneath the title are the words "A magazine for little children." The price is 25 cents. The cover picture of Eeny, Meeny, Miny, and Mo is by Martin; beneath is the couplet:

> All Life Is Full of Fun—Hurray!
> Who Cares for Care? Let's Laugh and Play.

Those lines set the tone for all the later issues. "Children want someone who will play with them," Martin said. "They want to play in their minds and their imaginations, just as my own wonderful mother played with me. . . . Most grown people have sat on their imaginations so long and so hard that they have crushed the life out of them. A child's beautiful world of Make-Believe is a place they don't even try to enter. Many children, knowing that average adults do not understand, live a whole secret existence in the world of Make-Believe. They are alone and unguided there. Yet it is the one realm where they can be most receptive and most responsive."

From the outset Martin had the able editorial assistance of Helene Jane Waldo, who remained with him until the magazine's final issue in 1933. Among the leading graphic artists who drew for *JMB* were the Gruelle brothers. Johnny Gruelle was the author and illustrator of the popular Raggedy Ann Books, and his brother Justin contributed even more frequently to *JMB,* not only art but also stories and verse. Jack Yeats, brother of William Butler Yeats, wrote and illustrated pirate tales. William Wallace Denslow, best known for his color plates in the first edition of L. Frank Baum's *Wonderful Wizard of Oz,* drew pictures for poems.

Another frequent contributor to *JMB,* both as a writer and artist, was Frank Verbeck, who illustrated Baum's *Magical Monarch of Mo.* In the April 1927 issue Wanda Gag—she became famous the following year for her best-seller *Millions of Cats*—published a clever story, "Bunny's Funny Easter Eggs," in which italicized words were used for solving a crossword puzzle.

The most important artist associated with *JMB* was George Carlson, a prolific illustrator who had been trained at the New York Academy of Design. A list of his books would run to almost a hundred titles. He drew for *St. Nicholas, Youth's*

Companion, Judge, Scribner's Magazine, Child Life, Famous Funnies, Jingle-Jangle Comics, and other periodicals, and for twelve years he was puzzle editor of the Girl Scouts' *American Girl.* Among the jackets he designed for adult novels was the jacket for the first edition of Margaret Mitchell's *Gone with the Wind,* still seen today on hardcover editions. Twenty-two years younger than Martin, Carlson was 75 when he died in 1962.

He became the magazine's most frequent cover artist, drawing more than fifty covers. He created almost all the magazine's puzzles, activities, jokes, and riddles, and an enormous variety of "gimmick" pages of a sort never before attempted in a child's magazine.

My own favorites as a child was Carlson's monthly page called "Peter Puzzlemaker." Martin introduced the feature (October 1918) by saying that he sometimes had to tell Peter his puzzles were too hard. "We want our puzzles to be just hard enough to make you work over them, but easy enough to solve before you get fidgety and impatient." In addition to a simple puzzle, each picture contained a mistake that you tried to find before the next issue revealed it. The mistakes were amusing and clever: a keyhole upside down, tallow dripping upward on a candle, a rake's handle that went behind a fist instead of through it, a star inside a crescent moon, an extra finger on a hand, smoke and a weather vane showing the wind blowing opposite ways, a cat without whiskers, a book with its title on the back cover, and so on.

A collection of these puzzle pages was issued by John Martin's House in 1922 as *Peter Puzzlemaker.* No better collection of puzzles for young children was ever published. Carlson's cartoon style has a refreshingly quaint period quality. It is unobjectionable to today's children who, like children in all ages, are indifferent to fashionable art trends. This new edition of *Peter Puzzlemaker* preserves all of the flavor and spirit of the original. The images and language in some of the puzzles have been revised to make them more accessible to children, and to reflect contemporary social values.

When Martin was interviewed in 1925 he said his magazine's circulation was 40,000. "I don't make money out of it. Most of my alleged salary as editor is turned back at the end of the year to help cover the customary deficit. I am the richest and happiest man on the earth, however, for my ledgers show a big profit in joy giving and getting."

John Martin died in 1947 at 82. An obituary in the *New York Times* disclosed that in 1900 he married Mary Elliott Putnam, who died in 1942. He had no children, except of course the scores of thousands who enjoyed his magazine, among whom I unashamedly count myself.

Adapted with permission from "John Martin's Book: An Almost Forgotten Children's Magazine," by Martin Gardner, in *Children's Literature* 18, ed. Francelia Butler, Margaret R. Higonnet, and Barbara Rosen (Yale University Press, © 1990 by The Children's Literature Foundation, Inc.).

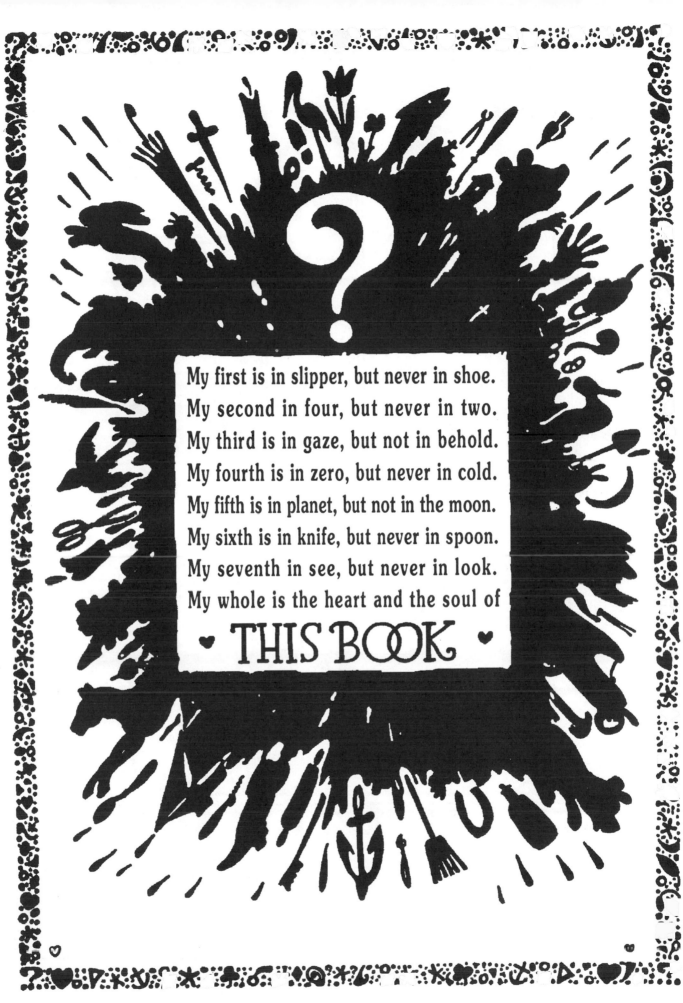

My first is in slipper, but never in shoe.
My second in four, but never in two.
My third is in gaze, but not in behold.
My fourth is in zero, but never in cold.
My fifth is in planet, but not in the moon.
My sixth is in knife, but never in spoon.
My seventh in see, but never in look.
My whole is the heart and the soul of
♥ THIS BOOK ♥

PETER PUZZLEMAKER keeps a store. The kind of store is in the panel in front of the counter. On the wall behind Peter is a list in Puzzlelandish of the things Anna Ostrich bought for her lunch. Ostriches like strange kinds of food.

Can you also find the mistake in the drawing?

A Riddle

I bought a ten-cent box of tacks
Down at the ten-cent store.
They were so very long and sharp,
What did I get them for?

The SIGN PUZZLE

OUR friend Peter Puzzlemaker is puzzled himself by Nickie Elf's sign, printed in Puzzlelandish. But Peter is a master in puzzles. He soon sees that Nickie had completely buried in letters a familiar quotation. What is it?

And what is the mistake, outside of the sign, in the picture?

A Question~

Julia likes to read her daily newspaper and does not miss a line. Do you know why they gave the paper the name "Watermelon"?

?

RIDDLES

WHAT is it that is a cat and not a cat, and yet is a cat?

Why is the letter G like the sun?

What goes from New York to Boston without moving?

RIDDLES

WHY is grass like a mouse?

Why is a dog's tail like the heart of a tree?

What is more wonderful than a horse that can count?

W HEN Alice went through Wonderland she met the caterpillar. She asked him how many words could be made using the letters in caterpillar. He said six. Alice knows at least twenty more. Can you find as many? Write them in the spaces on the picture.
Do you see the mistake in the picture?

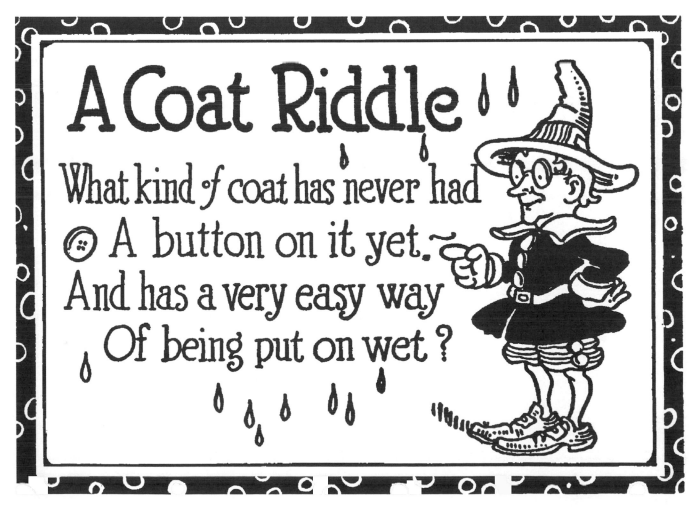

A Coat Riddle

What kind of coat has never had
A button on it yet,
And has a very easy way
Of being put on wet?

Ⓣⓗⓔ LUNCH PUZZLE

WHEN Peter leaves his shop, he likes to eat lunch where the menu is printed in Puzzlelandish. Peter thinks the menu sounds quite appetizing, because it begins with soup (SO UP) and pickles (PICK LESs). Can you find 13 things to eat hidden in the sign?

And do you see the mistake in the picture?

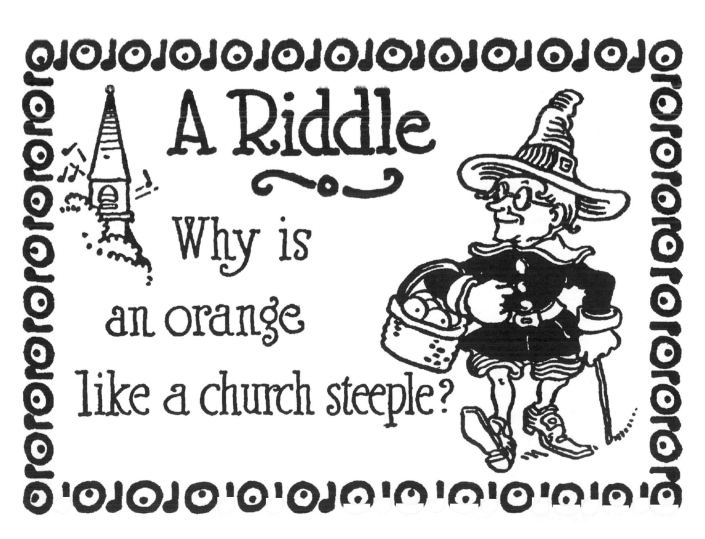

A Riddle

Why is an orange like a church steeple?

The Crab-Fishing Party

Occupation		Net
1. Hatter	1.	Bon<u>net</u>
2. Band Member	2.	
3. Professor in Insect Study	3.	
4. Astronomer	4.	
5. Carpenter	5.	
6. Electrician	6.	
7. Baby-Nurse	7.	
8. Musician	8.	
9. Jeweler	9.	
10. Poet	10.	

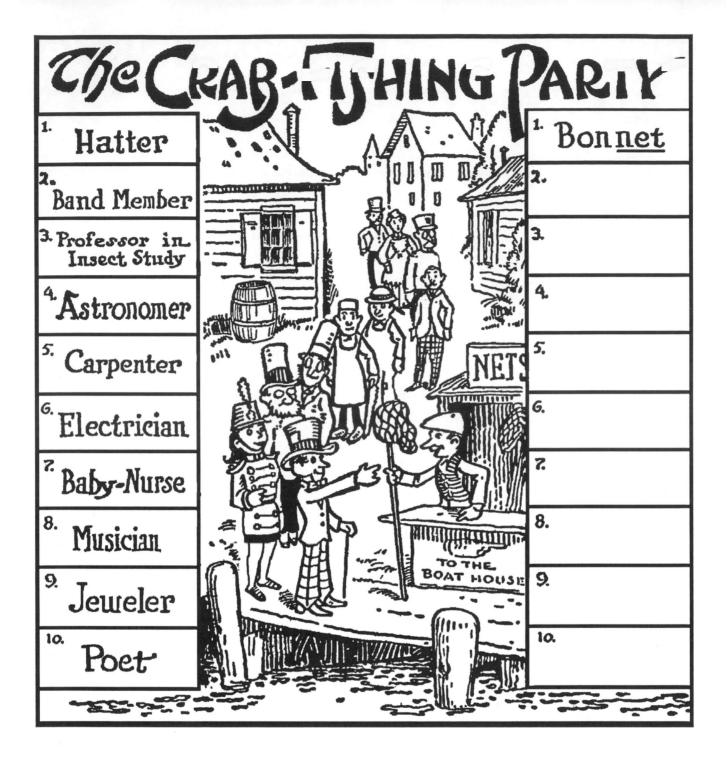

TEN people once made up a crab-fishing party and decided to fish with nets. The man who supplied the nets made jokes as he handed them out. "Ah," he said to the hatter, "You should have gotten a bonNET." He continued with his little jokes until he had supplied the whole line. On the left are the names of the people's occupations, and on the right you can fill in the kind of net that would be the best for each person.

THE ENTERTAINER AND HIS TRAINED ANIMALS

 TRAVELING entertainer had a trained dog, cat, and puppy, and they needed to cross a river. The boat was so small he could take only one animal at a time. The cat and the dogs would fight when the entertainer was not with them. If he left the big dog alone with the cat, the cat would get the worst of it, and if the puppy were left with the cat, the cat would tease the puppy. The two dogs could get along, however. How did the entertainer cross the river with the animals and avoid the fighting?

ETER bowls every evening with Geoffrey Elf. This evening, Peter painted letters on the pins and set them up to form a word. He will knock them down, one pin at a time, leaving a whole word every time a pin falls. There are seven words in all. How will he do it?

And what is the mistake in this picture?

A Question

Professor Starlight is trying to figure out if a fish lived in the sky, what kind of a fish it would be?

Do you know??

 N A bright corner of his garden, Peter has some beautiful sun-flowers. He calls the spot his Name Garden. Each flower has a name hidden in it, but to make a puzzle Peter has changed one letter in each name. Try to change them back again.

Also find the mistake in the picture.

SOME FUNNY QUESTIONS

 DO YOU suppose the person who invented the toothbrush had only one tooth? Otherwise, wouldn't it be called a teethbrush?

Are squirrels afraid of the bark of a tree?

When the sun shines in May, is it a mason?

If the front legs of a horse are fore (4) legs, doesn't it have six legs in all?

If a grand piano is made of mahogany, is a baby grand piano made of mapigany?

Can flowers be arrested for carrying pistils (pistols)?

SOME FUNNY QUESTIONS

IF A toad lives in the grass, is it a grasshopper?

Does the bed of a stream always have sheets of water over it?

Does a catfish have four paws and a furry tail?

What kind of wood is the multiplication table made of? Can you eat your breakfast off it?

If a fish has scales why doesn't it weigh itself?

Since crackers are baked in a hot oven, shouldn't they come out fire crackers?

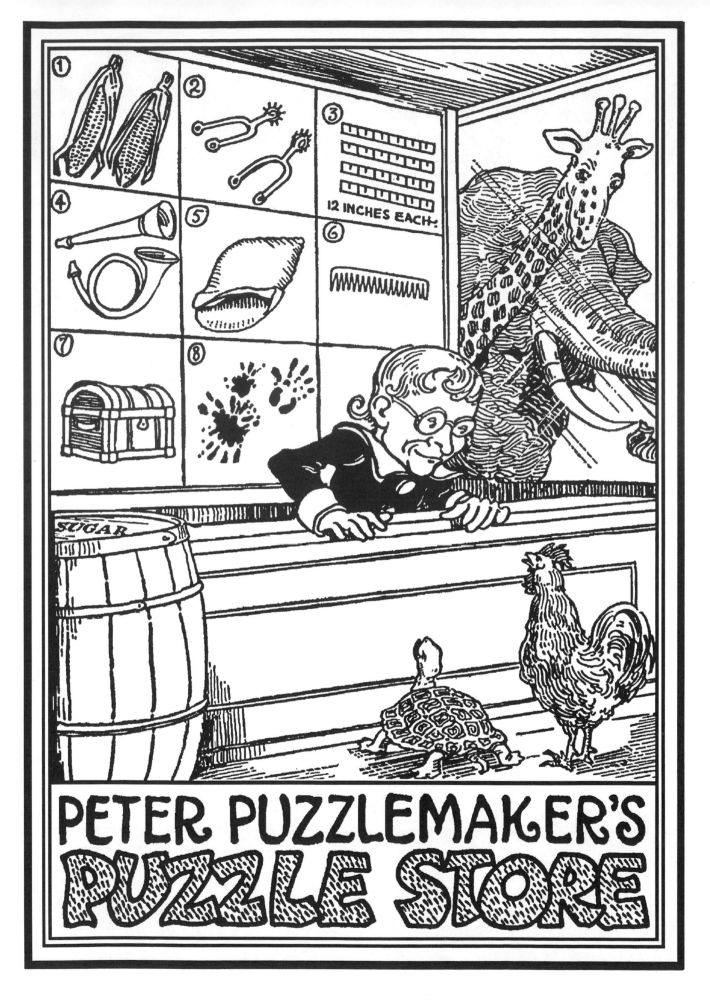

The PUZZLE STORE

PETER does a good business in his puzzle store. Each of the four customers in the picture demands exactly two things for life and happiness. These things are pictured behind Peter's counter. What are they?

And what is the mistake in the picture? (It's not in the sign.)

A Dog Riddle ~

If a dog should lose its tail, where would it get another?

PETER PUZZLEMAKER AND HUMPTY-DUMPTY

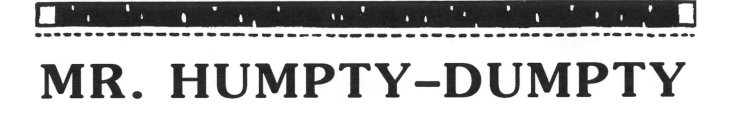

MR. HUMPTY-DUMPTY

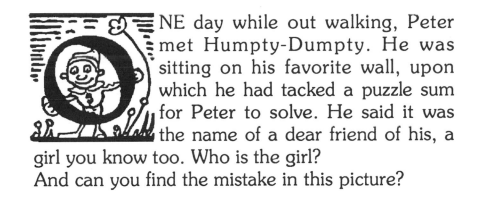NE day while out walking, Peter met Humpty-Dumpty. He was sitting on his favorite wall, upon which he had tacked a puzzle sum for Peter to solve. He said it was the name of a dear friend of his, a girl you know too. Who is the girl?

And can you find the mistake in this picture?

FILL IN THE MISSING WORD

PETER PUZZLEMAKER'S GARDEN PUZZLE

ᵺe GARDEN PUZZLE

RAISING vegetables has always been Peter Puzzlemaker's pride. Along the trellis he has pictured eight of the vegetables he grows in his garden. Can you tell what they are?

And what is the mistake in this picture?

A Hidden Name

I counted twelve nice big tulips in Adrian's garden

(A CITY)

PETER PUZZLEMAKER and the
SAILOR'S PUZZLE

The SAILOR'S PUZZLE

YESTERDAY Peter Puzzlemaker found two pieces of driftwood, and he is curious to know the meaning of the carvings. With the help of a sea captain, he discovers how to turn the ten words into names of things familiar to sailors by changing one letter in each word. Can you?

Now go digging for the mistake in the picture.

A Ship Riddle

My first is a vehicle,
my second is a preposition
and my whole is
part of a ship.

AUNT SUSAN'S QUILT

HEN Aunt Susan started to make a patchwork quilt for Julia's bed, she intended to make a large square by piecing together nine smaller squares. Before she finished, one square was lost and she could not find another to complete the quilt. But Julia sees a way to make a perfect square by cutting the cloth into four pieces with two straight cuts and joining them again. How is it done?

The BAKER

AND THE 4 HUNGRY KIDS

A BAKER baked a delicious raisin cake and sold a quarter of it. The cake was a square, and the piece cut from it was also a square. Four hungry kids enter the shop to buy the rest of the cake. The baker wants three dollars for it, but the kids have only two dollars. As it is the youngest boy's birthday, the baker will let them have the cake for two dollars if they can tell him how to cut it into four pieces of exactly the same size and shape. How will they get the cake?

PETER PUZZLEMAKER'S AUTO PUZZLE

ꚛThe AUTO PUZZLE

PETER PUZZLEMAKER made a trip around the world in his faithful old car. What could be better than to find, on his way back, a car puzzle written on a sign? Each of the eight pictures represents a part of an automobile.

And what is the funny mistake in this drawing?

Will he catch or miss the boat?

He misses it!

Take Peter through the maze and see if you can help him to catch the boat.

TO THE BOAT

How does Peter get home?

 RAVELING around the world, Peter Puzzlemaker found a strange puzzle that isn't in a book, but growing out in the open under the sky. It is a maze made of green hedges that have been growing for more than 225 years. The puzzle is to find the one path that will take you from the entrance to the center where the house stands. Can you find it?

OFTEN, on a stormy winter evening, Peter reads in his cozy library. He has found an interesting book, and on the open page you will find eight words, one hidden in each line. Each word represents a part of a book.

There is a mistake in the drawing. Do you see it?

· A Riddle ·

There is a word
I have in view,
Five letters it contains.
And if I should
Take out but two,
Then only one remains

1. _____ (WHERE THE STAIRS ARE)
2. _____ (NOT HIGH)
3. _____ (MEANS US)
4. _____ (VERY SMALL)
5. _____ (TO BE IN DEBT)
6. _____ (LAYS EGGS)
7. _____ (BY YOURSELF)
8. _____ (NOT OLD)
9. _____ (GARDEN TOOL)
10. _____ (FULL OF WATER)
11. _____ (PART OF A HOUSE)

PETER PUZZLEMAKER'S HALLOWEEN CATS

ℭhe CATS' PUZZLE

EACH Halloween, Peter Puzzlemaker gets his puzzle cats together for an evening of fun. This time he has put letter signs on them, and he finds he can make at least 11 words by separating and rearranging the nine cats. Maybe you can make more than 11 words. Can you find the funny mistake in this picture too?

Three Games
are represented
in this picture ~
K
·D·o·M·
What are
they ?

PETER PUZZLEMAKER'S
FLOWER GARDEN

ℭℎ𝔢 **FLOWER GARDEN**

IN the wall of his garden, Peter has made pictures of the flowers he will plant in the spring. He remembers seeing these flowers in his grandparents' garden. Can you name them?

There is something missing in the picture which Peter should know about. Can you find it?

A Question -

Sebastian dug a hole 3 feet long, 2 feet wide, 3 feet deep. Can you tell exactly how much earth there is in it?

?

A BEDTIME MOTTO

PETER likes helpful mottoes and has printed one in Puzzlelandish over his fireplace. He is reading it on his way to bed. Can you read it?

Peter says there is a mistake in this picture and wonders if you can find it.

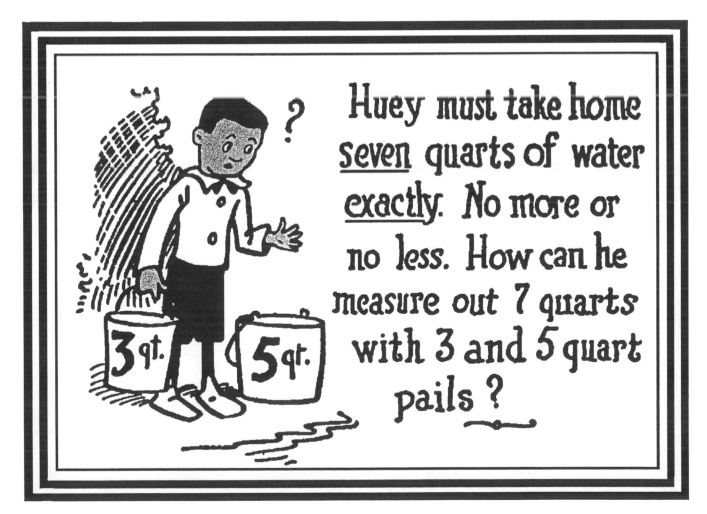

Huey must take home **seven** quarts of water **exactly**. No more or no less. How can he measure out 7 quarts with 3 and 5 quart pails?

3 qt. 5 qt.

RIDDLES

What is the first thing you set
in your garden?

Why are fish well educated?

What kind of a cat will you find
in a library?

RIDDLES

A duck before two ducks, a duck behind two ducks, and a duck between two ducks. How many ducks are there in all?

Why is the letter A like twelve o'clock?

How many bowls of soup can a giant eat on an empty stomach?

TEA

(LOTS OF WATER)

(TO USE A NEEDLE)

(A CARPENTER'S TOOL)

(NOT COOKED)

(TO MOVE A BOAT)

(TO STEAL)

(A BONE)

(A SAIL)

(A DANCE)

(AN ANIMAL)

PIE

PETER PUZZLEMAKER'S
TEA and PIE PUZZLE

The TEA AND PIE PUZZLE

ETER PUZZLEMAKER is treating a few friends to tea and a fine pie. He has a puzzle for them. By changing one letter at a time, he can turn TEA into PIE in eleven changes. Below the spaces you will find hints to help you.

What is the funny mistake in this picture?

FLOUR

———

———

———

———

———

BREAD

MAKE *the word* FLOUR *into* BREAD *in six changes.*

ℭ𝔥𝔢 FISHING PUZZLE

FISHING is one of Peter Puzzlemaker's favorite sports, and he often spends a vacation with a rod and line. If you do a little adding and subtracting of the puzzle sum, you will find out what kind of fish he is after.

Perhaps you can also discover the mistake in this picture.

A Hidden Name ~
We sailed smoothly along
as the sea then seemed
very calm.

(A CITY)

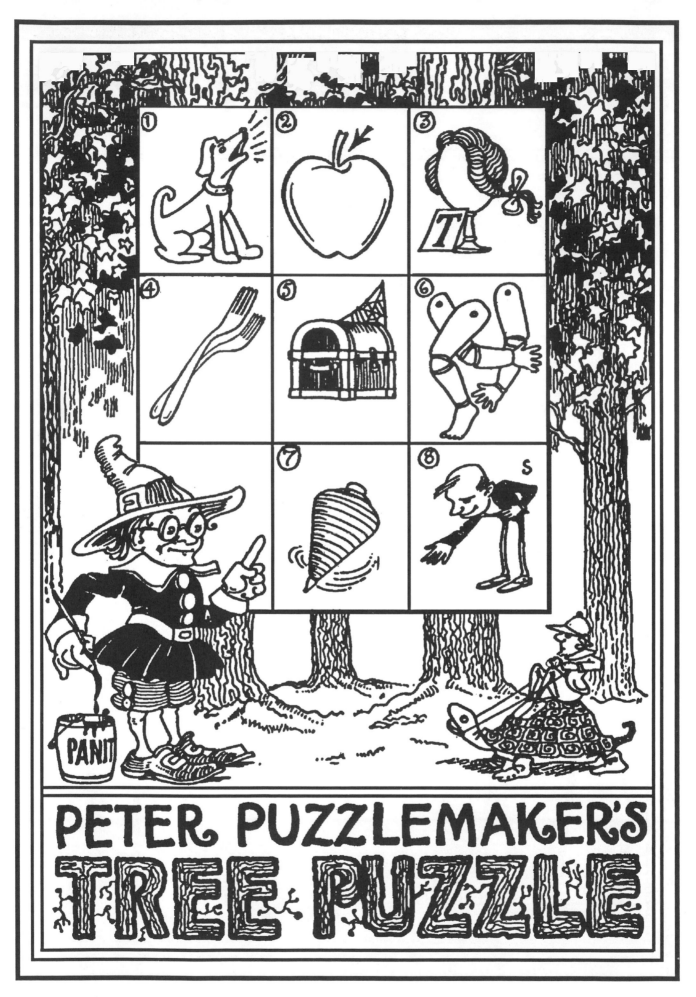

ᵀʰᵉ TREE PUZZLE

 **S**TANDING in the woods, Peter is trying to bewilder you with his eight pictures. Each picture conceals some part of a tree. Can you figure them out?
And there is a mistake somewhere else in the picture.

1. AN INSECT
2. MUSICAL INSTRUMENT
3. A ROMAN GARMENT
4. A PILE
5. A LARGE BOAT
6. AN ANIMAL
7. A METAL
8. WRITING INSTRUMENTS
9. SKIN OF FRUIT
10. THOUGHT
11. CLOSE TO
12. UNLIT
13. OUR SUN IS ONE
14. THREE
15. HELPS
16. A FLOWER

PETER PUZZLEMAKER'S
WORD·MILL

☞ℯ WORD-MILL PUZZLE

HIS strange windmill Peter calls his Word-Mill because he is going to paint a word puzzle on its wings. Put a letter on each square to make four-letter words that can be read both down and across. The meanings of the words are in the list. Number 1 is MOTH.
Do you see the mistake in the drawing?

FILL IN THE MISSING WORD

YOU WILL

ONCE MORE

A FAVOR TO

THAT

TELL ME THE NAME OF

PETER has just met his friend Anita, who is earnestly fishing in a pail. Anita tells Peter she feels sure there are fish in the pail because she has just thrown in a can of sardines. She also says she knows the names of the fish on the puzzle sign. Do you?

What is the mistake in this picture?

SEED

(USED IN WINTER)

(RAN AWAY)

(WHAT THE BIRD DID)

(WHAT THE WIND DID)

(TO MAKE COFFEE)

(WORKERS ON A SHIP)

(A BLACK BIRD)

CROP

PETER PUZZLEMAKER'S
FARM·PUZZLE

ARMER BROWN has asked Peter how the *crop* comes from the *seed*. He showed Peter a puzzle board and said it is done by changing one letter at a time in eight changes. Can you fill in the blanks?
And do you see the funny mistake in this picture?

PUT *the word* PIG *into* STY *in five changes.*

PIG

_____

_____

_____

_____

STY

MORE than a hundred objects on this page begin with the letter *B*. How many can you find?

The GLAZIER

AND HIS WINDOW PUZZLE

A GLAZIER works with glass. This glazier has made a window with 36 panes of glass. His customer wants to change 12 of the panes to red glass. The customer insisted that only two red panes should be in a straight row, either up and down, across, or diagonally. Two of the panes are already in, so one diagonal row is finished. Can you darken the squares where the other ten panes should go?

Peter Puzzlemaker ∾ 63

PETER PUZZLEMAKER'S
BIG "T" PUZZLE

The BIG "T" PUZZLE

PETER PUZZLEMAKER, while on a walking trip through China, came across this puzzle. The black pieces put together should make a perfect T. Trace them carefully and see if you can fit them into the white space as easily as Peter did. Can you find the mistake in this picture?

A Hidden Name ~

We always steer for that wharf in landing at this point.

(A COUNTRY)

The METEOROLOGIST

PETER'S friend, the village weather prophet (called a meteorologist), has just told him that he gets all his information from a book. Work out the puzzle sum by adding and subtracting the names of the pictures, and the answer will be the name of this wonderful book.

Something is wrong in the picture. Can you discover what it is?

WET
____
____
____
____
DRY

MAKE *the word* WET, DRY *in five changes.*

ℭℏℯ MISSING WORD

IN Wonderland, Peter has just met Alice's friend, the carpenter. He is crying because he cannot find the missing word that goes in the blank space. Put in the name of a city in New Jersey, and read from "the brand" and around the circle to "yesterday" and you will have a complete sentence.

Find the strange mistake in this picture too.

FILL IN THE MISSING WORD

My first is something baby wears,
My next, where we sleep well.
My third is that which keeps us clean,
My last the school hours tell

PETER PUZZLEMAKER AND THE 13 MATCHES

The THIRTEEN MATCHES

ERE Peter has taken 13 matches and is trying to make the four words told about in the riddle verse above him. The making of each word takes 13 matches, and each word begins with the letter *B*.

There is a mistake somewhere in this picture also.

PETER PUZZLEMAKER'S
PUZZLE SUM

The PUZZLE SUM

PETER has made a puzzle sum for Sara Elf to solve. See if you can find the answer too. Write down the names of the pictures, and add and subtract according to the plus and minus signs. The answer is the name of an animal.

There is a funny mistake in this picture too.

1. A WINGED CREATURE
2. THOUGHT
3. TO LEASE
4. A CERTAIN DAY
5. A SMALL SHIP
6. A VEGETABLE
7. UPPER LIMBS
8. WORK
9. OPPOSITE WEST
10. SPACE
11. SEA MAMMAL
12. TO SPEAK
13. TIE A _____
14. ONE AND 8
15. ONE TIME
16. 13-19
17. DOOR HANDLE
18. BACK of THE NECK
19. NOT CLOSED
20. NOT STRAIGHT

PETER PUZZLEMAKER'S WORD·CROSS

OHNNY ELF has made a puzzle he calls a Word-Cross. He wants Peter to put in four-letter words which will read two ways, down and across. The meanings of the words are on the paper hanging from the tree. Beginning with Number 1, Peter wrote BIRD.

Can you tell what is wrong in this picture?

PETER PUZZLEMAKER and THE PIEMAN

The PIEMAN PUZZLE

 IMPLE SIMON met not only the pieman but also Peter Puzzlemaker. The pieman has rigged up a set of pictures to show the kinds of pie he has for sale. Can you solve the pieman's puzzle?

There are two mistakes in this picture. Can you find them?

A Hidden Name

I found that my new rubber lined rain coat kept me quite dry-

(A CITY)

I CONSIDER BUYING DUNLAP A RISKY VENTURE.

NOVEMBER LINGERS IN THE LAP of WINTER.

WHEN SHE MARKED IT "O.K." YOU SMILED AND SAID "THANK YOU."

THE MEN WHO WENT TO WAR SAW UNFORGETABLE THINGS

THE ENTOMOLOGISTS FOUND IN THE BUD A PEST THAT DESTROYED THE BLOOM.

PETER PUZZLEMAKER and the
HIDDEN CITIES

BALLOONING is a sport Peter Puzzlemaker is quite fond of. He is sailing far above the housetops, and his mind is on the cities below him. The names of five big cities are hidden in the strange floating message. Can you find them?
And what mistake do you see in the picture?

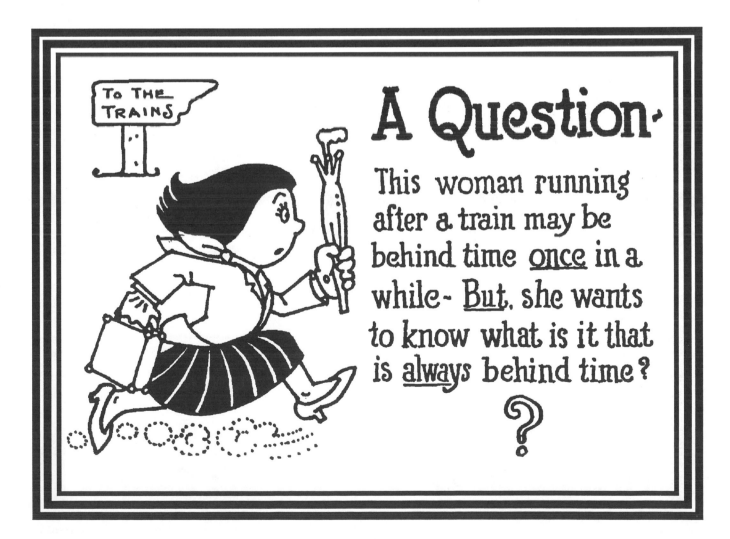

To THE TRAINS

A Question·

This woman running after a train may be behind time <u>once</u> in a while· <u>But</u>, she wants to know what is it that is <u>always</u> behind time?

PETER PUZZLEMAKER AND THE BOOKWORM

The BOOKWORM PUZZLE

WHILE Peter Puzzlemaker was in a bookshop, a bookworm asked this question: "I wiggled through a set of books from page 1 of Volume 1 to page 100 of Volume 12. Each of the 12 volumes was 1 inch thick, with 100 pages. How many inches did I crawl?"

A mistake is in this picture also.

A State Riddle

My first is a game, my second is what we use our eyes for, my whole is a Southern State.

These are some Riddles that I know

Here is a Puzzle that I made up myself

AND now that we have reached the end,
    I want to tell each little friend
How joy and thanks have filled my heart
To know you all have done your part
To solve the problems, great and small,
Each quiz and puzzle, one and all.
With patience, thought, and skillful care
You've played the game both fair and square.

But then before I'm really through,
One problem more I have for you.
My first, a part I know must be
Of creatures in the deep blue sea.
My second is, I know by far
A different form of "be" and "are."
My whole, a word of language past,
In many books is printed last.

❀ ANSWERS ❀

PAGE 2   Verse

We are not printing the verses, but will give you the key: The last word in the paragraph is the second word in the verse, the second word in the paragraph is the third word in the verse; by reading in this see-saw manner, you will read the verses, one verse to a paragraph.

PAGE 7   Blot

Puzzles.

PAGE 9   The Store Sticker

1. Hammer. 2. Crowbar. 3. Shoehorn. 4. Keys. 5. Scales. 6. Bolts. 7. Nail. 8. Screwdriver.

Name on counter: Harp - P = Har + Dwarf = Hardwarf - F + E = Hardware.

Mistake: The ostrich has one toe too many.

A Riddle

Ten cents.

PAGE 11   The Sign Puzzle

Follow the yellow brick road.

Mistake: Peter has one finger too many on his right hand.

A Question

Because the inside is always read (red).

PAGE 12   Riddles

1. A kitten.
2. Because it is the center of light.
3. Railroad track.

PAGE 13   Riddles

1. Because the cat'll eat it (cattle eat it).
2. Because it is farthest from the bark.
3. A spelling bee.

PAGE 15   The Caterpillar

Cat, pair, pill, carpet, ape, rat.

Mistake: Peter's umbrella is upside down.

A Coat Riddle

A coat of paint.

PAGE 17   The Lunch Puzzle

1. Soup. 2. Pickles. 3. Meat. 4. Ham. 5. Potato. 6. Roll. 7. Carrots. 8. Bread. 9. Butter. 10. Jam. 11. Pears. 12. Pie. 13. Tea.

Mistake: The letters on the weather vane are in the wrong places. E should be opposite W, and N should be opposite S.

A Riddle

Because we get a peel (peal) from it.

PAGE 18   The Crab-Fishing Party

1. BonNET. 2. CorNET. 3. HorNET. 4. PlaNET. 5. CabiNET. 6. MagNET. 7. BassiNET. 8. ClariNET. 9. GarNET. 10. SonNET.

PAGE 19   The Entertainer

First he takes the cat over, leaves it, and returns. Then he takes the puppy over and returns with the cat. He leaves the cat on the shore, takes the dog over to where the puppy is, and then returns and takes over the cat.

PAGE 21   The Seven Pins

Planets, planet, plane, plan, pan, an, a.

Mistake: Stars should not be inside a crescent moon.

A Question

A starfish.

PAGE 23   The Name Garden

Berry=Terry, Sun=Sue, Bell=Bill, And=Ann, Joke=Jose, Let=Lee, Kid=Kim, Any=Amy.

Mistake: Peter is not holding the rake.

A Hidden Name

Canada.

PAGE 24–25   Some Funny Questions

Peter Puzzlemaker says there are no real answers to these. Maybe you can think of a funny way to answer them, such as: "If the toothbrush inventor had had two teeth, we would call it a 2th brush." Or, "Only wild flowers should be arrested."

PAGE 27   The Puzzle Store

Rooster bought (6) comb and (2) spurs.
Turtle bought (5) shell and (3) four feet.
Elephant bought (7) trunk and (1) ears.
Giraffe bought (8) spots and (4) horns.
Mistake: Giraffes have two horns, not three.

A Dog Riddle

At a retail store.

PAGE 29   Mr. Humpty-Dumpty

Cone + Stall = Conestall + Ink = Conestallink - link = Conestal - Nest = Coal - Co = Al + Ice = Alice.

Mistake: Humpty-Dumpty has two left ears.

Missing Word

ME AT, or MEAT.

PAGE 31   The Garden Puzzle

1. Spinach. 2. Leek. 3. Endives. 4. Peas. 5. Potatoes. 6. Beets. 7. Cauliflower. 8. Cabbage.

Mistake: The smoke and the weather vane show the wind blowing in opposite directions.

A Hidden Name

Venice.

PAGE 33   The Sailor's Puzzle

Shop=ship, tail=sail, ripe=rope, boot=boat, wand=wind, wake=wave, later=water, dock=deck, charm=chart, dish=fish.

Mistake: The flag blows one direction and the chimney smoke blows the other.

A Ship Riddle

Cab-in.

PAGE 34   Aunt Susan's Quilt

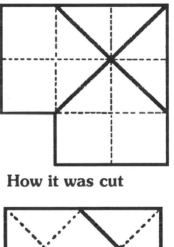

How it was cut

How it was joined

The dark lines show where it was cut, and the dotted lines show the patches.

PAGE 35
The Baker and the 4 Hungry Kids

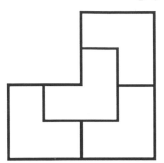

PAGE 37   The Auto Puzzle
1. Brake shoe. 2. Axle. 3. Top. 4. Springs. 5. Hood. 6. Horn. 7. Tire. 8. Gear.
Mistake: The steering wheel is not connected to the car.

Missing Word
CAR GO, or CARGO

PAGE 38   Will He Catch the Boat?
To catch the boat, keep to the right wherever you can.

PAGE 39   How Does Peter Get Home?
If you were walking, you could find your way by always keeping your right hand touching the hedge as you walked.

PAGE 41   The Book Puzzle
1. Cover. 2. Title. 3. Story. 4. Binding. 5. Page. 6. Word. 7. Type. 8. Picture.
Mistake: The wax on the candle is dripping the wrong way.

A Riddle
Stone—one.

PAGE 43   The Cats' Puzzle
1. Hall. 2. Low. 3. We. 4. Wee. 5. Owe. 6. Hen. 7. Alone. 8. New. 9. Hoe. 10. Well. 11. Wall.
Mistake: Two cats are missing whiskers.

Three Games
1. Tag. 2. Dominoes. 3. Croquet (crow-K).

PAGE 45   The Flower Garden
1. Pansy. 2. Dandelion. 3. Hollyhock. 4. Foxglove. 5. Rose. 6. Carnation. 7. Larkspur. 8. Tulips.
Mistake: The sprinkling can has no holes in its spout.

A Question
None; being a hole, it is empty.

PAGE 47   A Bedtime Motto
"Early to bed and early to rise makes a man healthy, wealthy, and wise."
Mistakes: Peter's shadow is in the wrong direction, and there seems to be nothing behind the andirons to hold up the logs.

A Question
First he filled the 5-quart pail and poured it into the 3-quart pail. Then he emptied the 3-quart pail and poured the remaining two quarts into the 3-quart pail. Then he filled the 5-quart pail again, so he had seven quarts.

PAGE 48   Riddles
1. Your foot.
2. Because they swim in schools.
3. A CATalog.

PAGE 49   Riddles
1. Three.
2. Because it is in the middle of the day.
3. One, after which the giant's stomach is no longer empty.

PAGE 51 The Tea and Pie Puzzle

Tea, sea, sew, saw, raw, row, rob, rib, jib, jig, pig, pie.

Mistake: The handles on the teapot and cups are upside down.

Flour into Bread

Flour, floor, flood, blood, brood, broad, bread.

PAGE 53 The Fishing Puzzle

Heart + Rope = Heartrope - H = Eartrope + Nut = Eartropenut - Ear = Tropenut - Pen = Trout.

Mistake: The line is attached to the fishing rod in the wrong place.

A Hidden Name

Athens.

PAGE 55 The Tree Puzzle

1. Bark. **2.** Stem. **3.** Twig. **4.** Forks. **5.** Trunk. **6.** Limbs. **7.** Top. **8.** Boughs.

Mistake: "Paint" on the can is misspelled.

A Hidden Name

Peru.

PAGE 57 The Word-Mill Puzzle

1. Moth. **2.** Oboe. **3.** Toga. **4.** Heap. **5.** Ship. **6.** Hare. **7.** Iron. **8.** Pens. **9.** Rind. **10.** Idea. **11.** Near. **12.** Dark. **13.** Star. **14.** Trio. **15.** Aids. **16.** Rose.

Mistake: The door to the mill has two doorknobs.

Missing Word

DO ME, or DOME.

PAGE 59 The Fish Puzzle

1. Sunfish. **2.** Shark. **3.** Pike. **4.** Herring. **5.** Carp. **6.** Catfish. **7.** Perch. **8.** Skate.

Mistake: The pail's reflection is wrong.

A Riddle

Drop it a line.

PAGE 61 The Farm Puzzle

Seed, sled, fled, flew, blew, brew, crew, crow, crop.

Mistake: The farmer has a boot on one foot and a shoe on the other.

Pig into Sty

Pig, pit, sit, sat, say, sty.

PAGE 62 Find the Bs

baby	bat	bit
baby bottle	bay	blacksmith
baby carriage	bay window	blade
back	beach	blanket
background	beacon	blinders
bacon	beak	blinds
badge	bear	blossoms
bag	beard	board
baggage	beast	boat
baker	bed	body
bakery	bedroom	bonnet
balcony	beef	book
bale	beets	boot
ball	belfry	bootblack
balloon	bell	bottle
balustrade	bellows	bough
bananas	belt	bouquet
bandage	bench	bow
banjo	berries	bowl
banner	bib	bowler
barber	bicycle	bowsprit
bark	bifocals	box
barn	bill	boy
barrel	billows	bracelet
basin	biplane	braces
basket	bird	bracket

braid	bridle	bundle
brake	brig	buns
branch	brook	buoy
branch	brush	bureau
bread	bubbles	bush
bread	bucket	butcher
bricks	buggy	butterfly
bridge	buildings	buttons

PAGE 63 The Glazier

PAGE 65 The Big "T" Puzzle

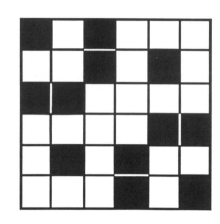

Mistake: The birds are flying upside down.

A Hidden Name
Finland.

PAGE 67 The Meteorologist

Signal + Man = Signalman + Ace = Signalmanace + Yes = Signalmanaceyes - Sign = Almanaceyes - Eyes = Almanac.

Mistake: N for north on the weather vane should be W for west.

Wet into Dry
Wet, bet, bat, bay, day, dry.

PAGE 69 The Missing Word
NEW ARK, or NEWARK.

Mistake: The clouds are behind the sun and its rays.

The Missing Word
MAN GO, or MANGO.

PAGE 71 The Thirteen Matches

Mistake: Peter has six fingers on his left hand.

Mine the Coal
Mine, mint, mist, most, moat, coat, coal.

PAGE 73 The Puzzle Sum
Turkey - EY = Turk + Eye = Turkeye - Key = Ture + Heart = Tureheart + L = Tureheartl - He = Tureartl + E = Tureartle - Ear = Turtle.

Mistake: The turtle seems to have six legs.

Two Animals
Tiger and alligator.

PAGE 75   The Word-Cross Puzzle

1. Bird. 2. Idea. 3. Rent. 4. Date.
5. Boat. 6. Okra. 7. Arms. 8. Task.
9. East. 10. Area. 11. Seal. 12. Talk.
13. Knot. 14. Nine. 15. Once. 16. Teen.
17. Knob. 18. Nape. 19. Open.
20. Bent.   Mistake: The flag is upside
down.

Two Famous Americans
Washington and Adams.

PAGE 77   The Pieman Puzzle

1. Walnut. 2. Cherry. 3. Gooseberry.
4. Raisin. 5. Mince. 6. Apple. 7. Pumpkin.
8. Peach. 9. Custard.
Mistakes: The pieman's bell has no clapper,
and the S in his sign is backwards.

A Hidden Name
Berlin.

PAGE 79   The Hidden Cities
Paris, Berlin, Tokyo, Warsaw, Budapest.
Mistake: The balloon ropes should not go
into the gas bag.

A Question
The back of a clock.

PAGE 81   The Bookworm Puzzle
Page 1 of Volume 1 is where the tip of
Peter's hat feather is pointing, and page
100 of Volume 12 is where the bookworm's
hat feather is pointing, making ten inches in
all.
Mistake: The title on the book Peter is
holding is on the back cover instead of the
front cover.

A State Riddle
Tennessee (tennis-see).

PAGE 86   Answer to Verse
Finis.